true
SPIRITUALITY
according to JESUS

A proven pathway to become like Jesus

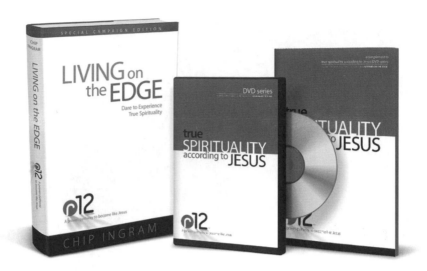

small group study guide

Welcome to the r12 small group study guide. This interactive six-week study is designed to help you explore the concepts of r12 with a group of friends. Each session has a 12–15 minute video teaching segment from Chip Ingram. You can buy a DVD of the video teaching and corresponding book, Living on the Edge at **LivingontheEdge.org/r12**.

While the book, *Living on the Edge*, comes at the topic of true spirituality from the teachings of the apostle Paul in Romans 12, this small group study looks at true spirituality according to Jesus.

We all know the power of personal example and modeling. Jesus not only taught about true spirituality, but he modeled it for us in His life and actions. Jesus didn't just point us to the WAY, His life **is** the WAY to True Spirituality.

> ## To order a copy of the *Living on the Edge* book,
> ## go to **LivingontheEdge.org/r12**

true spirituality according to Jesus

table of contents

ⓡ12

true spirituality™

how to start your own r12 small group

The fact that you are even reading this page says a lot about you. It says that you are either one of those people who has to read everything, or you are at least open to being used by God to lead a group.

Leading a small group can sound intimidating, but it really doesn't have to be. Think of it more as gathering a few friends to get to know each other better and to have discussions about spiritual matters.

Here are a few practical tips to help you get started.

1. **Pray.** One of the most important principles of spiritual leadership is to realize you can't do this on your own. No matter how long we've been leading, we need the power of the Holy Spirit. Lean on Him…He will help you.

2. **Invite some friends.** Don't be afraid to ask people to come to your group. You will be surprised how many people are open to such a study, especially when you let them know that the study is only for six weeks. Whether you have four or fourteen in your group, it can be a powerful experience. You should probably plan on at least an hour and a half for your group meeting.

3. **Get your materials.** You will need to get a DVD of the teaching done by Chip Ingram. You can get the DVD from **www.LivingontheEdge.org/r12**. Also, it will be helpful for each person to have his/her own copy of the book, *Living on the Edge*. Reading the book during the weeks of the small group study will enrich the discussion and learning for everyone.

4. **Be prepared to facilitate.** Just a few minutes a week in preparation can make a huge difference in the group experience. Each week, preview the video teaching and review the discussion questions. If you don't think your group can get through all the questions, select the ones that are most relevant to your group. Also, for each week, there is a two- to three-minute coaching segment just for leaders. This brief segment will help you know what to expect for that week.

5. **Love your group.** Maybe the most important thing you bring to the group is your personal care for them. If you will pray for them, encourage them, call them, e-mail them, involve them, and love them, God will be pleased and you will have a lot of fun along the way.

We know you can do this!

But if you need a little more guidance, we have prepared some online video coaching for you at **LivingontheEdge.org/smallgroups**. There you will find answers to the most common questions
about leading a group, including:

- I'm not a Bible expert; what if I get asked a question I can't answer?

- How much time do I need to spend preparing for our group meeting?

- What are the most important things I need to do as the group leader? And, what can I delegate to others?

- What are some tips for effectively facilitating group discussion?

- What things can "kill" a group? (Or, what are five ways to get people to stop coming to your group?)

- What should our group do about childcare?

- What do I do about "difficult" people in my group?

Thank you for your availability. May God bless you as you
serve Him by serving others.

true spirituality™

how to get the most out of this experience

You and your group are about to begin what could be a life-changing journey in your small group. This powerful study of True Spirituality in the life of Jesus provides some breakthrough teaching about what it means to be an authentic follower of Jesus Christ.

Listed below are the segments you will experience each week as well as some hints for getting the most out of this experience.

TAKE IT IN (During this section you will watch the video teaching)

Each teaching segment is 12-15 minutes long. A teaching outline with fill-ins is provided for each session. As you follow along, write down questions or insights that you can share during the discussion time.

Also, bring your Bible each week.

TALK IT OVER

Several discussion questions are provided for your group to further engage the teaching content. Keep the following guidelines in mind for having a healthy group discussion.

- **Be involved.** Jump in and share your thoughts. Your ideas are important, and you have a perspective that is unique and can benefit the other group members.

- **Be a good listener.** Value what others are sharing. Seek to really understand the perspective of others in your group and don't be afraid to ask follow up questions.

- **Be courteous.** Always treat others with utmost respect. When there is disagreement, focus on the issue and never turn the discussion into a personal attack.

- **Be focused.** Stay on topic. Help the group explore the subject at hand, and try to save unrelated questions or stories for afterwards.

- **Be careful not to dominate.** Be aware of the amount of talking you are doing in proportion to the rest of the group, and make space for others to speak.

- **Be a learner.** Stay sensitive to what God might be wanting to teach you through the lesson, as well as through what others have to say.

 **LIVE IT OUT**

These simple suggestions help the lesson come to life. Don't ignore them; give them a try! Check in with another group member during the week and ask how it's going.

 VIDEO FAQs

These sessions will certainly raise additional questions. We have tried to anticipate some of those questions. At the end of each session there are 3 additional questions that Chip has briefly answered on video. These answers can be seen online at **www.LivingontheEdge.org/r12**

true spirituality™

what is

how do you measure a disciple?

☑ **pray**

☑ **tithe**

☑ **read the bible**

☑ **serve others**

☐ **follow Jesus**

True Spirituality ?

To participate in this small group study, you will need a DVD of Chip's teaching and copy of the book, *Living on the Edge*.

Before you watch the video, discuss the following two questions:

1. What are some popular ideas and definitions of true spirituality?

2. How would you define a "good Christian"?

 **TAKE IT IN (WATCH THE VIDEO)**

Today there is a lot of confusion within the church about true spirituality.

- In Romans 12 we learn the principles of true spirituality.

- In Jesus we have a portrait of true spirituality.

…fixing our eyes on Jesus, the author and perfecter of faith…

Hebrews 12:2a (NASB)

Three Critical Questions Every Believer Must Answer:

1. How did Jesus define true spirituality?

2. How did Jesus model true spirituality?

3. What does Jesus demand of us on the path to true spirituality?

Jesus replied: *"'Love the Lord your God with all your heart and with all your soul and with all your mind.' This is the first and greatest commandment. And the second is like it: 'Love your neighbor as yourself.'"*   Matthew 22:37–39 (NIV)

1. **Jesus defines true spirituality by** _____ .

   • True spirituality is NOT religious activity or keeping religious rules.

   • True spirituality is loving God and loving people.

   The question you need to ask and answer is, How is your love relationship with Jesus Christ?

   He who has My commandments and keeps them is the one who loves Me; and he who loves Me will be loved by My Father, and I will love him and will disclose Myself to him.   John 14:21 (NASB)

2. **Jesus defines true spirituality by** _____ .

   Jesus answered, "I am the way and the truth and the life. No one comes to the Father except through me."   John 14:6 (NIV)

   • The Way—the Path

   • The Truth—the Teacher

   • The Life—the Source and Creator

   Jesus' life is the way to true spirituality.

   I am not ashamed of the gospel, because it is the power of God for the salvation of everyone who believes: first for the Jew, then for the Gentile. For in the gospel a righteousness from God is revealed, a righteousness that is by faith from first to last, just as it is written: "The righteous will live by faith."
   Romans 1:16–17 (NIV)

   If you want to receive Christ as your savior and become His follower, share that decision with your group leader. If you still have questions, you can watch a brief video from Chip about what it means to become an authentic Christ follower. The video can be found at www.LivingontheEdge.org/newstart

Have you put your trust in Christ or in your religious activity?

3. Jesus offers true spirituality _____.

Come to Me, all who are weary and heavy-laden, and I will give you rest. Take My yoke upon you and learn from Me, for I am gentle and humble in heart, and you will find rest for your souls.

Matthew 11:28–29 (NASB)

True spirituality is a life of rest, refreshment, and joy.

 **TALK IT OVER**

1. Reflect back on your spiritual roots. Where did your ideas about true spirituality come from?

2. During this session, Chip shared the gospel and its power to change lives. Take a few minutes and have some in your group share the story of how they came to faith in Christ.

3. Over the course of your life, who or what has had the most impact on your spiritual growth?

4. How would you describe your spiritual growth over the last five years? When did you grow the most? When have you struggled?

5. Brainstorm as a group and make a list of at least ten examples from the life of Jesus when he modeled true spirituality…loving God and loving people.

6. Read Matthew 22:37–39 and answer the following question. If you decided to really make this the definition of true spirituality, how would it change you?

Jesus replied: "'Love the Lord your God with all your heart and with all your soul and with all your mind.' This is the first and greatest commandment. And the second is like it: 'Love your neighbor as yourself.'"

LIVE IT OUT

1. Spend some time this week reading through portions of the Gospels (Matthew, Mark, Luke or John). As you read, keep the following question in mind: how is Jesus modeling true spirituality? *(If you are not sure where to read, start with Mark, chapters 1–9).*

2. In your book, read the first section, "How to Give God What He Wants the Most," before your next group meeting.

3. This series could shape your life in significant ways. Will you commit to participating in this group for all six sessions?

? **VIDEO FAQs**

You can find Chip's brief answers to the following questions by going to
www.LivingontheEdge.org/r12

1. I think I'm a Christian, but I have my doubts. Can I really know for sure?

2. If true spirituality isn't about rules or religious activity, why do so many Christians and churches make those the acid test for being a "good Christian"?

3. What is the role of the Holy Spirit in true spirituality?

SESSION 2
GIVING GOD
what He

wants THE MOST

Therefore, I urge you, brothers, in view of God's mercy,
to offer your bodies as living sacrifices, holy and
pleasing to God-- this is your spiritual act of worship.
Romans 12:1 (NIV)

TAKE IT IN (WATCH THE VIDEO)

Therefore, I urge you brothers, in view of God's mercy, to offer your bodies as living sacrifices, holy and pleasing to God—this is your spiritual act of worship.
Romans 12:1 (NIV)

1. What did Jesus teach us about surrender and true spirituality?

- Surrender is the _____ to experiencing true spirituality.

I tell you the truth, unless a kernel of wheat falls to the ground and dies, it remains only a single seed. But if it dies, it produces many seeds. The man who loves his life will lose it, while the man who hates his life in this world will keep it for eternal life.
John 12:24–25 (NIV)

- Jesus teaches surrender as the _____ through which God's biggest and best blessings flow.

2. How did Jesus model surrender as the pathway to pleasing the Father?

Though he was God, he did not think of equality with God as something to cling to. Instead, he gave up his divine privileges; he took the humble position of a slave and was born as a human being. Philippians 2:6–7 (NLT)

- Jesus surrendered even before he came to earth. The first surrender is one we never see.

*Jesus gave them this answer: "I tell you the truth, the Son can do **nothing** by himself."*
John 5:19a (NIV)

*By myself I can do nothing; I judge only as I hear, and my judgment is just, for I seek **not to please myself** but him who sent me.*   John 5:30 (NIV)

- Jesus' _____ was marked by surrender.

- Jesus' _____ on earth was marked by surrender.

Going a little farther, he fell with his face to the ground and prayed, "My Father, if it is possible, may this cup be taken from me. Yet not as I will, but as you will."
                                                                    Matthew 26:39 (NIV)

Surrender is the _____ element in the church today.

3. **What is Jesus saying to you about surrender in your life?**

Then he said to them all: "If anyone would come after me, he must deny himself and take up his cross daily and follow me. For whoever wants to save his life will lose it, but whoever loses his life for me will save it."   Luke 9:23–24 (NIV)

The problem is not that He is asking too much; the problem is that we are believing too little.

For the LORD God is a sun and shield;
The LORD gives grace and glory;
No good thing does He withhold from those who walk uprightly.
                                                                    Psalm 84:11 (NASB)

Are you "all in"? Make Jesus Lord…TODAY.

 **TALK IT OVER**

1. When you were growing up, what was your view of God? What was he like? **How have you come to believe in God's goodness?**

2. Who is the most committed Christ follower you have ever known? What is it about his or her life that is different?

3. Read the passage below and answer the following questions.
   In this passage, what principles can we learn from Jesus teaching about surrender? Practically speaking, what would it look like for you to "put your hand to the plow" and not look back when it comes to following God?

   As they were walking along the road, a man said to him, "I will follow you wherever you go." Jesus replied, "Foxes have holes and birds of the air have nests, but the Son of Man has no place to lay his head."

   He said to another man, "Follow me." But the man replied, "Lord, first let me go and bury my father." Jesus said to him, "Let the dead bury their own dead, but you go and proclaim the kingdom of God."

   Still another said, "I will follow you, Lord; but first let me go back and say good-by to my family." Jesus replied, "No one who puts his hand to the plow and looks back is fit for service in the kingdom of God."   Luke 9:57–62 (NIV)

4. Read Hebrews 12:2 (NIV).
   *Let us fix our eyes on Jesus, the author and perfecter of our faith, who for the **joy** set before him endured the cross, scorning its shame, and sat down at the right hand of the throne of God.*

   Surrender is not easy, but it is the pathway to joy. After Jesus surrendered to the cross, what was the "joy set before him"? What joy (or satisfaction) is there in surrendering to God?

5. What are the biggest barriers that keep you from making a total commitment to Jesus Christ? Is there some area of your life that is not surrendered to the lordship of Jesus?

6. Are you willing to surrender each and every area of your life to the lordship of Christ? Spend the last few minutes of your group time in prayer. Offer prayers of surrender, letting God know that you are "all in."

 **LIVE IT OUT**

1. Sometime during this week, write out a prayer of surrender. Set aside enough time to carefully consider your prayer. If you need some help getting started, consider sincerely praying this prayer of surrender below:

Dear Jesus,

I want to thank you for loving me and dying for me. You know all of my faults and flaws and yet you still want a relationship with me. I am so grateful that you have saved me and forever changed me. I owe you everything.

So, today I want to declare my total commitment to you and tell you that "I'm All In". I don't want to hold anything back… I belong to you. All that I have and all that I am I surrender to you as the leader of my life.

Today and from this day forward I want you to be Lord over my career, over my family, over my money, over my relationships, over my time, and over my future.

I know that you are a good and loving Father and that you know what is best for me. So, I submit to your purposes even when I don't understand or when I can't see what you are doing. I choose YOUR way because I believe YOUR way is best.

2. Share your prayer with a trusted friend.

3. God is not a cruel taskmaster. He is a loving father who knows that surrender is the pathway to great blessing. Memorize and meditate on Psalm 84:11 (NIV) this week:

> *For the LORD God is a sun and shield;*
> *the LORD bestows favor and honor;*
> *no good thing does he withhold*
> *from those whose walk is blameless.*

4. This week, pray for the others in your group by name. Pray that they would have the courage to fully surrender to God.

5. In your *Living on the Edge* book, read the second section, "How to Get God's Best for Your Life," before your next group meeting.

VIDEO FAQs

You can find Chip's brief answers to the following questions by going to
www.LivingontheEdge.org/r12

1. Is surrendering to Christ's lordship the same as becoming a Christian?

2. In my heart, I really have surrendered to Christ, but I still find myself lapsing back into sins that keep me defeated. What should I do?

3. Surrender feels scary and radical. What are some of the common barriers that keep ordinary Christians like me from surrendering?

getting the
very

best
from GOD

Do not conform any longer to the pattern of this world, but be transformed by the renewing of your mind. Then you will be able to test and approve what God's will is—his good, pleasing and perfect will..
Romans 12:2 (NIV)

TAKE IT IN (WATCH THE VIDEO)

Do not conform any longer to the pattern of this world, but be transformed by the renewing of your mind. Then you will be able to test and approve what God's will is—his good, pleasing and perfect will. Romans 12:2 (NIV)

1. **What did Jesus say about true spirituality in a** _____ **world?**

What good is it for a man to gain the whole world, and yet lose or forfeit his very self? Luke 9:25 (NIV)

- Jesus taught that we are in a real battle with Satan and a world system designed to _____ our lives.

2. **How did Jesus model "the way" of victory over the world's temptations?**

- The 1st Temptation—Lust of the Flesh

"If you are the Son of God, tell these stones to become bread." Matthew 4:3b (NIV)

Jesus answered, "It is written: 'Man does not live on bread alone, but on every word that comes from the mouth of God.'" Matthew 4:4 (NIV)

- The 2nd Temptation—Pride of Life

Then the devil took him to the holy city and had him stand on the highest point of the temple. "If you are the Son of God," he said, "throw yourself down." Matthew 4:5–6 (NIV)

Jesus answered him, "It is also written: 'Do not put the Lord your God to the test.'" Matthew 4:7 (NIV)

- The 3rd Temptation—Lust of the Eyes

Again, the devil took him to a very high mountain and showed him all the kingdoms of the world and their splendor. "All this I will give you," he said, "if you will bow down and worship me." Matthew 4:8–9 (NIV)

Jesus said to him, "Away from me, Satan! For it is written: 'Worship the Lord your God, and serve him only.'" Matthew 4:10 (NIV)

3. What is Jesus saying to you about how to overcome the world system?

Jesus was saying to those Jews who had believed Him, "If you continue in My word, then you are truly disciples of Mine; and you will know the truth, and the truth shall make you free." John 8:31–32 (NASB)

- Your mind is transformed by the _____.

- Your mind is renewed when you

> Hear God's Word
> Read God's Word
> Study God's Word
> Memorize God's Word
> Meditate on God's Word

So What?

1. Where do you need to say "no" to the world?

2. How do you need to say "yes" to the Word?

The more your heart turns *to* Jesus, the more your heart will turn *from* the world.

TALK IT OVER

1. In your mind, where have Christians violated Scripture and been swept along by the culture? Give some specific examples.

2. In John 17 Jesus said that we are not *of* the world but that he did send us *in* to the world. What does it mean for Christ followers today to be *in* the world, but not *of* the world?

3. Share a time in your journey when the world's values made it difficult for you to follow God. How did you get through it? What did you learn?

4. Where is the world squeezing you into its mold? What specific strategies does the enemy use that tempt you the most?

5. Read the passage below and discuss the following questions: What does it look like in your everyday life to "remain" in Jesus? How is the analogy of "vine and branches" a good picture of our relationship with Christ?

Remain in me, and I will remain in you. No branch can bear fruit by itself; it must remain in the vine. Neither can you bear fruit unless you remain in me. I am the vine; you are the branches. If a man remains in me and I in him, he will bear much fruit; apart from me you can do nothing.

John 15:4–5 (NIV)

6. What is the biggest hindrance to you spending time in God's Word on a regular basis?

7. What step will you commit to taking in order to more fully engage God's Word?
   - ☐ Have daily time alone with God and His Word
   - ☐ Spend more time reading the Bible
   - ☐ Memorize a passage of scripture
   - ☐ Begin to listen to biblical teaching on CD
   - ☐ _____

 **LIVE IT OUT**

1. Give up all forms of media for forty-eight hours (tv, radio, iPod, Internet). Ask a friend or family member to do this with you. Commit to pray for one another and to hold each other accountable. Consider having your entire group do this together this next week.

2. Have a discussion with your family or with a good friend about this week's session. Spend some time talking about the impact of media on our lives and how we should respond as Christ followers.

3. Decide to get up twenty minutes earlier each day for the next two weeks to spend time with God and His Word. Find a partner who is willing to make the same commitment. You can share what you are learning and you can help each other follow through.

4. This week, consider memorizing Romans 12:2 (NIV):

Do not conform any longer to the pattern of this world, but be transformed by the renewing of your mind. Then you will be able to test and approve what God's will is—his good, pleasing and perfect will.

5. In your book, read the third section, "How to Come to Grips with the Real You," in preparation for your next group meeting.

❓ VIDEO FAQs

You can find Chip's brief answers to the following questions by going to **www.LivingontheEdge.org/r12**

1. I am really struggling with some addictive behavior. I just can't seem to say no to temptation. No one else really knows what is going on with me. What should I do?

2. My spouse is not a believer and we have very different values and standards. This is causing conflict in our relationship. How can I stand by my convictions without ruining my marriage?

3. The thought of reading the Bible seems intimidating. I don't know where to begin. Can you give me some tips on where and how to get started?

coming to grip

with the
real YOU

For by the grace given me I say to every one of you:
Do not think of yourself more highly than you ought,
but rather think of yourself with sober judgment, in
accordance with the measure of faith God has given you.
Romans 12:3 (NIV)

 **TAKE IT IN** (WATCH THE VIDEO)

For by the grace given me I say to every one of you: Do not think of yourself more highly than you ought, but rather think of yourself with sober judgment, in accordance with the measure of faith God has given you.
Romans 12:3 (NIV)

1. What did Jesus teach us about how we are to view_____?

For everyone who exalts himself will be humbled, and he who humbles himself will be exalted.
Luke 14:11 (NIV)

2. How did Jesus' life show us "the way" to obtain an accurate self-view?

- No one can give you an accurate view of your life, but _____ alone.

As soon as Jesus was baptized, he went up out of the water. At that moment heaven was opened, and he saw the Spirit of God descending like a dove and lighting on him. And a voice from heaven said, "This is my Son, whom I love; with him I am well pleased."
Matthew 3:16–17 (NIV)

While he was speaking, a cloud appeared and enveloped them, and they were afraid as they entered the cloud. A voice came from the cloud, saying, "This is my Son, whom I have chosen; listen to him."
Luke 9:34–35 (NIV)

- Every one of us needs someone else to tell us who we really are.

3. What is Jesus saying to you about your need for an accurate self-view?

From everyone who has been given much, much will be required; and to whom they entrusted much, of him they will ask all the more.　　　Luke 12:48b (NASB)

- I am _____.

I no longer call you servants, because a servant does not know his master's business. Instead, I have called you friends, for everything that I learned from my Father I have made known to you. You did not choose me, but I chose you and appointed you to go and bear fruit—fruit that will last. Then the Father will give you whatever you ask in my name.　　　John 15:15–16 (NIV)

- I am _____.

God has given each of you a gift from his great variety of spiritual gifts. Use them well to serve one another.　　　1 Peter 4:10 (NLT)

- I am _____.

For we must all appear before the judgment seat of Christ, that each one may receive what is due him for the things done while in the body, whether good or bad.　　　2 Corinthians 5:10 (NIV)

Someday I will stand before the judgment seat of Christ and God will ask me, "What did you do with what I gave you?"

So what?

- I must get into God's Word and understand who I am in Christ.
- I need a community of believers in my life who will help me have an accurate self-view.

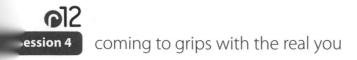

))) TALK IT OVER

1. What is the most powerful affirmation you can ever remember receiving?

2. What are the primary messages you received from your parents that have shaped your view of yourself?

3. Who or what are the top three people or events that have shaped how you view yourself today?

4. What is the biggest discovery you have made about yourself in the last five years?

5. Ephesians 2:10 (NLT) says, *For we are God's masterpiece. He has created us anew in Christ Jesus, so we can do the good things he planned for us long ago.*

   Honestly, how are you doing with accepting how God made you and who He made you to be?

6. If you could do anything for God, and time and money were not obstacles, what would you attempt?

7. Spend some time affirming one another. As you think about others in your group, complete the following statement: "What I appreciate most about you is…"

 **LIVE IT OUT**

1. Make it your mission this week to help people know how wonderfully created they are. Look for opportunities all week long to say to people, "I'm really glad God made you just the way He did…you are a gift to me." If you are a parent, you might want to write a letter of blessing to each of your kids.

2. Make a list this week of statements that are true about your identity in Christ. Spend some time with your Bible, seeking to discover what God says about you. Start with Psalm 139, Romans 8, and Ephesians 1.

3. If you are struggling to know where you are gifted, try this little exercise. Do a little informal survey (perhaps by e-mail) of people that know you well. Ask them this simple question: "Based on what I'm good at and passionate about, how could you see God using me to serve others?"

4. One of the best ways to discover where you are gifted and passionate to serve is to just start serving. Explore opportunities to serve in your church or community. Make a short-term commitment and dive in…you were made to serve.

5. In your book, read the fourth section, "How to Experience Authentic Community," in preparation for your next group meeting.

VIDEO FAQs

You can find Chip's brief answers to the following questions by going to **www.LivingontheEdge.org/r12**

1. I really struggle with self-esteem issues and often struggle with feeling insignificant. How do I begin to get victory over these feelings?

2. As a parent, what can I do to make sure my kids have an accurate self-assessment?

3. I'm not totally sure what my gifts are and where I should serve. What are some steps I should take to discover my unique gifts?

EXPERIENCING
authentic

community

*Love must be sincere. Hate what is evil; cling to what is good.
Be devoted to one another in brotherly love. Honor one another
above yourselves. Never be lacking in zeal, but keep your spiritual
fervor, serving the Lord. Be joyful in hope, patient in affliction,
faithful in prayer. Share with God's people who are in need.*
Romans 12: 9-13 (NIV)

experiencing authentic community

◉ TAKE IT IN (WATCH THE VIDEO)

Authentic community happens when the real you meets real needs for the right reason in the right way.

Love must be sincere. Hate what is evil; cling to what is good. Be devoted to one another in brotherly love. Honor one another above yourselves. Never be lacking in zeal, but keep your spiritual fervor, serving the Lord. Be joyful in hope, patient in affliction, faithful in prayer. Share with God's people who are in need. Practice hospitality. Romans 12:9–13 (NIV)

1. What did Jesus teach about authentic community?

A new commandment I give to you, that you love one another, even as I have loved you, that you also love one another. By this all men will know that you are My disciples, if you have love for one another. John 13:34–35 (NASB)

- The gospel is _____ by how deeply we love one another.

- Authentic community is at the _____ of Christianity.

…that they may all be one; even as You, Father, are in Me and I in You, that they also may be in Us, so that the world may believe that You sent Me. John 17:21 (NASB)

2. How did Jesus model "the way" to build authentic community in his life?

r12 Christianity is caught in _____.

When the hour came, Jesus and his apostles reclined at the table. And he said to them, "I have eagerly desired to eat this Passover with you before I suffer." Luke 22:14–15 (NIV)

Characteristics of Community:
>A place and time (They were intentional)
>A meal
>Singing
>Truth-telling
>Teaching
>Serving

Jesus knew that the Father had put all things under his power, and that he had come from God and was returning to God; so he got up from the meal, took off his outer clothing, and wrapped a towel around his waist. After that, he poured water into a basin and began to wash his disciples' feet, drying them with the towel that was wrapped around him. John 13:3–5 (NIV)

Now that you know these things, you will be blessed if you do them. John 13:17 (NIV)

- True community is not defined by a warm, fuzzy feeling. Rather, it is defined by _____ _____ ____ love.

3. What is Jesus saying to you about the depth and quality of your relationships?

Greater love has no one than this, that one lay down his life for his friends. John 15:13 (NASB)

So what?

- **Stop**…Examine the pace of your life and the depth of your relationships. Who do I need to go deeper with?

- **Look**…Pay attention to the needs of the people in your relational world. Who has some needs that you could meet?

- **Listen**…Ask God to show you who and where to serve in love. Where do I start?

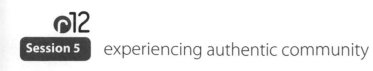

 **TALK IT OVER**

1. Describe the closest friendship you have ever had and what made that friendship so special.

2. What characteristics would you use to define authentic biblical community (fellowship)?

3. Share a time when you needed the support of your friends to make it through a difficult time? In what specific ways did they support you?

4. What are the biggest barriers to you experiencing deeper relationships?
   - ☐ Too busy
   - ☐ Job demands
   - ☐ Fear of rejection
   - ☐
   - ☐ Fear to initiate
   - ☐ Lack of intentionality
   - ☐ Past hurts
   - _____

5. As a group, brainstorm as many examples as possible of times when Jesus "noticed" and met a need.

6. Read Luke 10:30–37. In this story, what lessons can we learn from Jesus about meeting real needs for the right reason in the right way?

7. What is one tangible, practical, generous way that your group could serve someone in need? Make a plan and commit to following through.

 **LIVE IT OUT**

1. This week get in touch with someone who has provided true, authentic community in your life. Let that person know what the friendship has meant to you and how his or her life has impacted you.

2. This week personally do something that anonymously blesses someone in need. You will rediscover the joy and adventure of generosity.

3. Have an intentional conversation with a friend this week. Rather than talking about sports, weather, and politics, spend time talking about the more important things in life. For example, ask the following questions: What are your hopes for your kids? What concerns do you have about the future? Where are you personally struggling?

4. Every single day this next week pray for people in your group. Consider asking people for specific prayer requests, and then throughout your day, carry the needs of your friends to the Lord.

5. In your book, read the fifth section, "How to Overcome the Evil Aimed at You," in preparation for your next group meeting.

 **VIDEO FAQs**

You can find Chip's brief answers to the following questions by going to **www.LivingontheEdge.org/r12**

1. I really struggle with loneliness. Deep down I want to experience deeper relationships, but it feels risky. What advice would you give someone like me?

2. I belong to a small group, but it just seems like we are going through the motions. We study the Bible and we all get along, but we are not going deeper in our relationships. What would you suggest?

3. We have a couple of people in our small group that don't seem very committed. They miss our group meetings frequently and don't really carry any of the responsibility. What should we do?

overcoming

the

12
true spirituality™

aimed at
YOU

evil

Do not repay anyone evil for evil. Be careful to do what is right in the eyes of everybody. If it is possible, as far as it depends on you, live at peace with everyone. Do not take revenge, my friends, but leave room for God's wrath, for it is written: "It is mine to avenge; I will repay," says the Lord. On the contrary: "If your enemy is hungry, feed him; if he is thirsty, give him something to drink. In doing this, you will heap burning coals on his head." Do not be overcome by evil, but overcome evil with good.
Romans 12: 17-21 (NIV)

Session 6   overcoming the evil aimed at you

TAKE IT IN (WATCH THE VIDEO)

Do not repay anyone evil for evil. Be careful to do what is right in the eyes of everybody. If it is possible, as far as it depends on you, live at peace with everyone. Do not take revenge, my friends, but leave room for God's wrath, for it is written: "It is mine to avenge; I will repay," says the Lord. On the contrary:
"If your enemy is hungry, feed him;
if he is thirsty, give him something to drink.
In doing this, you will heap burning coals on his head."
Do not be overcome by evil, but overcome evil with good.
                                        Romans 12:17–21 (NIV)

1. What did Jesus teach is to be our response when evil is aimed at us?

You have heard that it was said, "Love your neighbor and hate your enemy." But I tell you: Love your enemies and pray for those who persecute you, that you may be sons of your Father in heaven.   Matthew 5:43–45a (NIV)

• Jesus taught that we are never more like _____ than when we return good for evil.

2. How did Jesus model "the way" we are to respond to the evil aimed at us?

Two other men, both criminals, were also led out with him to be executed. When they came to the place called the Skull, there they crucified him, along with the criminals— one on his right, the other on his left. Jesus said, "Father, forgive them, for they do not know what they are doing." And they divided up his clothes by casting lots.

The people stood watching, and the rulers even sneered at him. They said, "He saved others; let him save himself if he is the Christ of God, the Chosen One."

The soldiers also came up and mocked him. They offered him wine vinegar and said, "If you are the king of the Jews, save yourself."
                                        Luke 23:32–37 (NIV)

- Not only did Jesus (the creator) allow those he created to kill him, he even forgave them for doing it.

Be kind to one another, tender-hearted, forgiving each other, just as God in Christ also has forgiven you.   Ephesians 4:32 (NASB)

3. What is Jesus saying to you about your response to someone who has hurt you deeply?

Forgive us our debts, as we also have forgiven our debtors. And lead us not into temptation, but deliver us from the evil one.
                                                                    Matthew 6:12–13 (NIV)

How do we get there?

- _____ – a choice = a point in time decision

- _____ – a process = a journey of aligning our will and emotions

- _____ – a conclusion = rejoicing with their success

 **TALK IT OVER**

1. Spend some time sharing about any wound that you might still be carrying. How are you handling it? How does God want you to respond? How will you begin the forgiveness process?

Perhaps today's teaching has brought to the surface a painful situation you are facing right now. Don't be afraid to ask your group for prayer. You don't have to share the details, but you need the prayer and support of Christian friends. Spend whatever time is necessary to pray for those in your group who are dealing with relational wounds.

---

3. Read Ephesians 4:32 (NIV).
Be kind and compassionate to one another, forgiving each other, just as in Christ God forgave you.

How does understanding this verse help in forgiving someone who has hurt you?

3. Practically speaking, what does it look like to "bless" those who have hurt you?

4. If you are going to have a conversation with someone who has hurt you in the past, what are some precautions you should take?

(Watch Chip's closing challenge on video. Select "Wrap Up" on the DVD menu.)

Making r12 a "Way" of Life

These last three questions are designed to help you keep the r12 journey alive after this study is over.

1. What would change in your individual lives, your families, your group, and your church, if for the next 12 months you decided to live the "way" Jesus modeled for us to live?

2. How has this r12 journey impacted you? Over the next sixty days, what are the most important steps you can take to sustain the momentum?

3. If this group gathered back together one year from today, what would be the evidence that r12 has made a lasting impact on us?

🌱 LIVE IT OUT

1. If you have a wound that needs to be addressed, identify one trusted friend you can share this hurt with and ask him or her to walk with you.

2. If there is a person you need to forgive, make the choice today. Write it down with today's date. Share your decision with a friend and ask for his or her prayer and support.

3. Read through an entire gospel (Matthew, Mark, Luke, or John) this week. Pay attention to the "way" Jesus lived and the implications for the "way" we are to live.

4. Set aside a block of time this week to reflect on this r12 journey. Write down all the ways that this study has changed your perspective of the Christian life. Share your list with a friend or someone from your group this next week.

In the Bible, the people of God often kept a record of God's activity. If God has used this series to impact your life in some specific way, share your story at **www.LivingontheEdge.org**. Just click on the Share Your Story tab to get started.

VIDEO FAQs

You can find Chip's brief answers to the following questions by going to
www.LivingontheEdge.org/r12

1. What will happen if I just ignore any anger or hatred that I might have against someone?

2. How do I make something right with a person if the person has already died?

3. What are some practical ways that I can bless those that have been my enemies?

Jesus answered, "I am the way and the truth and the life.
No one comes to the Father except through me."
John 14:6 (NIV)

leader's notes

valuable resources for leaders to help facilitate group interaction and growth with r12 lessons

- group agreement

- tips for leading

- building relationships beyond
   your group meeting

- prayer & praise

- group roster

- what's next

group agreement

People come to groups with a variety of different expectations. The purpose of a group agreement is simply to make sure everyone is on the same page and that we have some common expectations.

The following Group Agreement is a tool to help you discuss specific guidelines together during your first meeting. Modify anything that does not work for your group, then be sure to discuss the questions on the next page under "Our Game Plan." This will help you to have an even greater group experience!

WE AGREE TO THE FOLLOWING PRIORITIES	
Take the Bible Seriously	To seek to understand and apply God's truth in the Bible
Group Attendance	To give priority to the group meeting (Call if I am going to be absent or late)
Safe Environment	To create a safe place where people can be heard and feel loved (no snap judgments or simple fixes)
Be Confidential	To keep anything that is shared strictly confidential and within the group
Spiritual Health	To give group members permission to help me live a godly, healthy spiritual life that is pleasing to God
Building Relationships	To get to know the other members of the group and pray for them regularly
Prayer	To regularly pray with and for each other
Other	

OUR GAME PLAN

- Will we have refreshments? _____

- What will we do about childcare? _____

- What day and time will we meet? _____

- Where will we meet? _____

- How long will we meet each week?_____

tips for leading your group

BEFORE THE GROUP ARRIVES

1. **Be prepared.** Your personal preparation can make a huge difference in the quality of the group experience. We strongly suggest previewing both the DVD teaching by Chip Ingram and the study guide.

2. **Pray for your group members by name.** Ask God to use your time together to touch the heart of every person in your group. Expect God to challenge and change people as a result of this study.

3. **Provide refreshments.** There's nothing like food to help a group relax and connect with each other. For the first week, we suggest you prepare a snack, but after that, ask other group members to bring the food so that they share in the responsibilities of the group and make a commitment to return.

4. **Relax.** Don't try to imitate someone else's style of leading a group. Lead the group in a way that fits your style and temperament. Remember that people may feel nervous showing up for a small group study, so put them at ease when they arrive. Make sure to have all the details covered prior to your group meeting, so that once people start arriving, you can focus on them.

TAKE IT IN (WATCH THE VIDEO)

1. **Get the video ready.** Each video session is clearly indicated on the DVD menu. Be sure to test your video equipment ahead of time and make sure you have located this week's lesson on the DVD menu.

2. **Watch the Group Leader Helps.** These brief 2-3 minute videos will provide specific coaching for each week's session as well as tips on facilitating an effective meeting.

3. **Have ample materials.** Before you start the video, also make sure everyone has their own copy of the study guide. Encourage the group to open to this week's session and follow along with the teaching. There is an outline in the study guide with an opportunity to fill in the outline.

3. **Arrange the room.** Set up the chairs in the room so that everyone can see the television. And, arrange the room in such a way that it is conducive to discussion.

 **TALK IT OVER**

Here are some guidelines for leading the discussion time:

1. **Make this a discussion, not a lecture.** Resist the temptation to do all the talking, and to answer your own questions. Don't be afraid of a few moments of silence while people formulate their answers.

   And don't feel like you need to have all the answers. There is nothing wrong with simply responding "I don't know the answer to that, but I'll see if I can find an answer this week".

2. **Encourage everyone to participate.** Don't let one person dominate, but also don't pressure quieter members to speak during the first couple of sessions. After one person answers, don't immediately move on; ask what other people think, or say, "Would someone who hasn't shared like to add anything?"

3. **Affirm people's participation and input.** If an answer is clearly wrong, ask "What led you to that conclusion?" or ask what the rest of the group thinks. If a disagreement arises, don't be too quick to shut it down! The discussion can draw out important perspectives, and if you can't resolve it there, offer to research it further and return to the issue next week.

   However, if someone goes on the offensive and engages in personal attack of another person, you will need to step in as the leader. In the midst of spirited discussion, we must also remember that people are fragile and there is no place for disrespect.

4. **Detour when necessary.** If an important question is raised that is not in the study guide, take time to discuss it. Also, if someone shares something personal and emotional, take time for them. Stop and pray for them right then. Try to keep the group on track, but allow the Holy Spirit room to maneuver, and follow his prompting when the discussion changes direction.

5. **Subgroup.** One of the principles of small group life is "when numbers go up, sharing goes down". So, if you have a large group, sometimes you may want to split up into groups of 3-5 for the discussion time. This is a great way to give everyone, even the quieter members, a chance to say something. Choose someone in the group to guide each of the smaller groups through the discussion. This involves others in the leadership of the group, and provides an opportunity for training new leaders.

6. **Pray.** Be sensitive to the fact that some people in your group may be uncomfortable praying out loud. As a general rule, don't call on people to pray unless you have asked them ahead of time or have heard them pray in public. But this can also be a time to help people build their confidence to pray in a group. Consider having prayer times that ask people to just say a word or sentence of thanks to God.

 **LIVE IT OUT**

These simple suggestions will help you apply the lesson. Be sure to leave adequate time to talk about these practical applications of the lesson. This is a great way to build group community. Try these ideas together and hold each other accountable for completing them, then share the following week how it went.

A FINAL WORD...

Keep an eye on the clock. Be sensitive to time. Whatever is the agreed upon time commitment, try to stick with it. It is always better to finish the meeting with people wanting "more" rather than people walking away stressed out because the meeting went long.

building relationships beyond your group meeting

1. **Be sure to collect everyone's name, e-mail and phone number.** This is so that the group can stay in touch with each other. Send out an e-mail list to everyone in the group.

2. **Get the group to interact outside the group**; encourage e-mailing or calling each other during the week to share good news, a prayer concern, or a lesson learned.

3. **Contact anyone who misses a group meeting**, and ask another couple of people to do so as well.

4. **Get together for at least one fellowship event apart from your group meeting.** This could be as simple as sharing a meal together

5. **Be sensitive to what is going on in the lives of your group...** (birthday, anniversary, illness, job interview). Use these as opportunities to bless them with notes, cards, or meals.

6. **Get others involved in order to give them a sense of ownership.** Ask for help with e-mailing prayer requests to the group, planning a fellowship event, leading the discussion, or providing the refreshments.

7. **Pray regularly** for each member of the group by name.

prayer & praise

One of the most important things you can do in your group is to pray with and for each other. Write down each other's concerns here so you can remember to pray for these requests during the week!

Use the Follow Up box to record an answer to prayer or to write down how you might want to follow up with the person making the request. This could be a phone call, an e-mail or a card. Your personal concern will mean a lot!

PERSON	PRAYER REQUEST	FOLLOW UP

prayer & praise

PERSON	PRAYER REQUEST	FOLLOW UP

prayer & praise

PERSON	PRAYER REQUEST	FOLLOW UP

prayer & praise

PERSON	PRAYER REQUEST	FOLLOW UP

prayer & praise

PERSON	PRAYER REQUEST	FOLLOW UP

prayer & praise

PERSON	PRAYER REQUEST	FOLLOW UP

group roster

	NAME	PHONE	EMAIL
1.			
2.			
3.			
4.			
5.			
6.			
7.			
8.			
9.			
10.			
11.			
12.			
13.			
14.			
15.			

what's next?

If your group would like to go deeper in their understanding of one of the five relationships in Romans 12, consider one of the following studies:

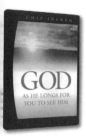

SURRENDER...
God, As He Longs for You to Know Him
How would you describe God? Awesome? All Powerful? Creator? While we cannot know Him exhaustively, we can know Him truly. And God longs for you to see Him as He truly is. Join Chip in this fascinating series studying seven attributes of God.

SEPARATE FROM THE WORLD...
Miracle of Life Change
Is life change really possible? If we're honest most of us would answer, 'No.' You've tried numerous programs that promise big changes, but in reality, deliver very little results. You long for transformation, but don't know where to begin. There's good news for you and there is hope. Life change is possible!

SOBER IN SELF-ASSESSMENT...
Your Divine Design
Do you know how God has uniquely wired you? Every believer was created to play a strategic role in the body of Christ with the gifts God has given them. But many of today's Christians face one difficult question—how do I discover my spiritual gifts and use them effectively in my church?

SUPERNATURALLY RESPONDING TO EVIL WITH GOOD...
Invisible War
Beneath our tangible landscape lurks an invisible spiritual realm where an unseen battle rages. It's real. And it's dangerous. If you're prepared to remove the blinders and gaze into the unseen world, Chip is ready to take you there.

All studies available at LivingontheEdge.org

If you want to be an r12 Christian...
START HERE.

Discover the profile of a disciple in a media rich online environment at r12 online.

A new online guided discipleship pathway from Living on the Edge based on Romans 12.
You can watch, journal, review message outlines, get coaching and more!

Online Videos

- Surrendered
- Seperate
- Self assessment
- Serving
- Supernaturally

Online Coaching

- Coaching ideas to help you teach others
- Get help and go deeper with additional resources

Journals & Outlines

- Message outlines & journal notes
- Reflection questions & journal notes

LivingontheEdge.org/r12